Marriage, and Other Science Fiction

Marriage, and Other Science Fiction

Albert Goldbarth

Ohio State University Press
Columbus

Library of Congress Cataloging-in-Publication Data
Goldbarth, Albert.
    Marriage, and other science fiction / Albert Goldbarth.
        p.   cm.
    ISBN 0-8142-0650-6 (cloth). — ISBN 0-8142-0651-4 (paper)
    I. Title.
PS3557.O354M37   1994
813'.54—dc20   94-10387
                                                            CIP

Text and jacket design by Hunter Graphics.
Type set in Berkeley Old Style by Brevis Press, Bethany, Connecticut.
Printed by Cushing-Malloy, Inc., Ann Arbor, Michigan.

The paper in this book meets the guidelines for permanence and
durability of the Committee on Production Guidelines for Book
Longevity of the Council on Library Resources. ∞

9   8   7   6   5   4   3   2   1

Acknowledgments

With thanks to the editors of the following journals for first publishing the poems found in this collection:

Agni Review: Fang

The Beloit Poetry Journal: 12,000 Bones of Frogs and Toads

Boulevard: Life Is Happy, (also reprinted in *The Best American Poetry: 1993*)

The Colorado Review: Cheese

Cream City Review: Stephen Hawking, Walking; Notes from the Desktop

Epoch: Doctor Nitty-Gritty; Acquisitions; Engravings in the Books of the 17th-Century Scientist/Mystic Athanasius Kircher (with an epigraph from a video catalogue)

The Laurel Review: A Slightly Shuffled History of Western Civilization, with Three Moons

The New England Review: The Counterfeit Earth!

The New Yorker: 'Zilla; Entire Lives

The Ontario Review: In Praise of the Bathos; The Emergence of Flight from Aristotle's Mud

The Paris Review: Marriage, and Other Science Fiction

Poet Lore: Mars

Poetry: The Amounts; Spaces; The Way the Novel Functions; Effect over Distance; Arguing Bartusiak; The Yoking of the Two Modes

Poetry East: Three Degrees of It

Poetry Northwest: Little, Big; Seriema Song

Western Humanities Review: A Blank Wide Face

Witness: Wrestling with Each Other

The Yale Review: Us / Claudia / Talleyrand

ᴑ

Lee Server's *Danger Is My Business* (Chronicle Books, 1993) originally brought my attention to the quotation that serves as epigraph.

for Skyler

not that all of these poems are autobiographical,
but that you're somewhere in all of my poems

Both my wife and myself are regular readers of your Wonder Stories, *and naturally there are lots of stories we read that call for discussion. I contend that it is impossible that in the future "time traveling" machines will be invented that will transport one through time to the future, say 1,000 years—and my wife says that it will be possible to do so. Who is correct?*

from a letter to the editor, 1931

Contents

Mars

Outside of town, near midnight,
I can always find that special point
on my dial where two far stations hit
congruently, so hot jazz
and a fundamentalist preacher say their
passions at once. I think of Mars

and what it must be like to live
below two moons. In books I read
as a teenager, someone always adventured out
of Marsport, over those crimson dunes, with double
the dose of high romance I ever expected
—although I've heard a woman and some

inner djinn of my own call to me simultaneously,
away from each other. Where's the point
in a rabbi where a wife and a God
both bed down? Isn't this what we call
science fiction?—someone
who can see by two lights.

Wrestling with Each Other

When the President declares the war over,
the other wars aren't over. The dust
is still at war with the subatomic needles
of electrical charge that stitch the flesh together.
The light is still at war with the sour dark
in the toe of the shoe. The woman besieges the man;
the man, the woman. The white; and the yolk.
When the Holy Benevolent Tyrant of Tyrants says
the bloody crusade is ceased, the opposition of Eternity
and History continues. That's not funny; and can't you
take a joke. Reality; and "reality." It's dawn, you
wake: mind rises into the body like sun
above the horizon. Another morning.
Fire; and water. Hook; and eye.

&

It's raining, a light gray skein of it, and
she sees this as the house's being woven
ever tighter into a viable notion of family. She
wants a child. She hugs herself at the window,
repeating the feel of that tightening weave
and everything it means: a nest,
I guess, comes close as a symbol. Meanwhile,
the weather is ruining his plans
for hunting dove this afternoon. I love
these friends of mine, and with the priceless coin
of their marriage I can't choose sides. He
doesn't want children. All day
it rains. The stream; and the bank.
The rush of flood; and stasis. All day and into the night.

4

In this 14th-century Sienese *Virgin and Child,* Mary
is stolidly shapeless under her mantle, certainly
her gold leaf chest is breastless, is as flat as the panel
it's painted on—and yet the infant suckles,
from a small flesh-colored ball the painter's set
against the gold and purple cloth around Her armpit,
so it is and isn't corporeal, so it might be something
pliant and taut and mammalian, something as veined
as a ball of blue cheese, something soapy and nubbled,
or might be just the brief, begrudged idea of this
in the overwhelming gold holiness of the scene.
The ageless incompatibility. One night: "You
creep, you only want me for my titties." The next: "*Now*
what's the matter? *Look*—doesn't this turn you on?"

♄

When the emir waves his feathered wand, declaring
the border skirmishes at an end, there's still that line
in quantum physics where the particles of "our" "time" meet
the tachyons of "backwards" "time," there's still
conflicting powers in our voids and sines and serums.
When the pasha and the brigadier sign their treaty,
God continues needing feuding with Darwin,
cop with robber, rust with iron, "truth" with "subjectivity."
It rains; it sounds like a tommygun on the roof.
The earthworms swell and slither. And then, of course,
the early birds. When clan and clan lay down their swords
beneath the Tree of Truce, even so, one still is drawn
to that line by Dickens: ". . . misery and magnificence
wrestling with each other upon every rood of ground in the prospect."

⌖

Mary, Mother of God and Secret Agent from Space, is
one scenario. Fantasy novels in which the Earth's
a war zone, and our species is the working-out
of another galaxy's battles, or another, eldermost
pantheon of dark deities'. Then every brachiate
dwindle or surge of our evolution, every noted
fascicle of devotion or gumption or dumbfuck luck
in History, is one more moving-forward
of foreign hostilities. Even the most benign of mornings
on the patio. Or we're warriors controlled by our genes.
Their needs. The tides of fortune, and the nucleotides.
The Cross. The cross look. Sun in the puddles
left by the rain. A man and a woman sitting down
to breakfast in that relentless machine.

♄

I've weighted the game: she *doesn't* want a child,
it's dissatisfaction airier, slipperier than this, though
no less painful when it stabs or when her own reflection
stares back from the window filled with thick gray weather
inside her skull. He *doesn't* bag dove: I couldn't pass up
that mild bird with the olive branch
heraldically nipped in its beak. But
their distress is true. The rain and whatever
pall of contention it's come to mean is true,
and will return, with all of its fierce life
and erasure. It will be here at the end,
whatever the dialogue, it will have the last word.
It was here at the origin, stirring the mix.
The first sex on Earth was division.

☾

Hegemony; and the subaltern. Particle; and wave.
The neocortex; and the hypothalamus. Honey;
bitter herb. Having spoken just now to both of them,
I set the phone back in its plastic cradle
as if it could explode. When every military wallah
lauds the ways of peace, the lamb beside the lion,
there will still be my two friends. My head
is feverish with their bicker, a simmer
of helplessness won't leave my brow,
and I lean my head against the cool,
the impartial, glass of the window—feeling it leach
this fever away, with the press of its clarity.
And, from the other side: the tapping,
the reminding, almost the arguing now, of the rain.

'Zilla

It's twilight in the streets of the tabletop Tokyo, and
the tabletop atrocity unconcernedly ambles over a retaining wall
—the baddest of all, the highest nabob of filmdom's many saurian
nemeses. Skyscrapers unconstruct like pop-apart toy kits,
lengthy commuter trains get whipped about like tire chains. And
we believe this scale-model world is real, or real enough—one lesson
from the science of those days is that we've tampered overmuch with
        nature; now
when atom-smasher blasts release this creature's city-stomping
        rampage, it
seems credible that for our reckless hubris the universe
punishes us. Seems credible—desirable. Yes, better that
than science's other mid-century revelation: we're a micropuff
of something-motes that float up the slipstream of nothing. Flesh
is energy bonded tentatively from nothing. God is a fiction
compounded of nothing. Structure, time, fate—nothing. Better

☿

retaliation than that. At least retaliation means
a watchfulness is set upon our days—"I am
a jealous and a vengeful Lord," and suddenly our no-dance
in the anti-halls of null-space has an orderliness. Just ask this
slippery six-year-old who's pilfered his way through his
        mother's neglected
handbag and is seven rumpled dollar bills, eight nickels, and a cigarette
richer, swaggering with his loot to school for a block, then
stepping carefully the next block as a black scad of misgivings
starts to mass, and finally slinking the rest of the way
beneath a sky grown attentive and baleful, a storm-sky
in a cosmos that we necessarily see as having form, as being
stimulus and consequence in their recurrent duet.
Without this . . .   well, my sweet friend J, old stoic but open
friend of forty-five, admits he's lonely without the geometry

        ⚭

of a wife (or any approximation) making the proper
angles of containment in an otherwise unshaped day.
"I start to talk to myself" amid the scattered glassware,
and the smoking pipes like marks of exotic punctuation
littered from the sky. "That's not *so* bad, J." "Oh, I talk, I
hum, I start to dribble out of myself like those fluids you see
in shots of antigravity during astronaut training, I . . ."
even that sentence trails oozily off. He watches the waters
cover the beach, then snap back, like a magician's tablecloth,
cover, then back . . .   Is it two in the morning? three?
Meanwhile, across town, she's confronting the child over
her opened purse goddamit, and where's philandering daddy
when she needs him goddamit to hell. She shudders. She feels
the monster inside her begin to test the locks of its resting place.

In Praise of the Bathos

Workmen drained the lake below the Roller Coaster at Blackpool's
Pleasure Beach to find hundreds of pairs of false teeth that had fallen
from the mouths of screaming passengers.

unattributed news clipping

Immediately, the fine, rose line of sunrise is as solid as a shawl
thrown over the shoulders of Chichén Itzá. In 1904, in the jungled
heat there and the chill of the limestone shadows, Edward
     Thompson starts,
in part by dredge and in part by terrified diving, seven years
     of reclamation
of artifacts out of the famous Sacrificial Well. The drop is sixty feet,
to sixty feet of ropily slime-choked water and forty more of shifting
guck. From this, on March 11, the jiggle of *pom*—of resin incense—
"the size of a baseball" lumpishly appears and, soon, the rest
of the splendid, testamentary fragments of a way of life and its deaths
begin appearing: dart-throwers (also darts) of obsidian;
plaques of jade and discs of low-grade alloy gold; flint chisels;
masks; cups; copper bells; and yellowed skulls and ribs, of victims
given over now for 1500 years to the mineral interwork
of bone and water. When I remember the week I thought I was dying

     ⚛

(awaiting the blood tests, scrutinizing every cankerette of each
purported symptom under the magnifying lens of my imagination)
I sometimes set that puff of death-thought in relief against the
        background-scale
vastness of the horror at the Well, the way against its crowded gallery
of darkly godcharged remnants I might set recovered
dentures from the lake of Blackpool's Pleasure Beach—that is,
with honest fondness. History squanders its dramas; an individual
needs to conserve and condense. And so I'd easily believe
a 'coaster groundscrew worker pockets one—that amphitheater
of fake teeth pinkly domed—and keeps it, fingers it in secret
talismanically, and understands the high-mode indication
of human hungers and human loss it comes to represent in its own
low-mode vaudevillian way. Of those two poles, most lives that I know
circle the second. Edward Thompson said, referring

♁

to his suited exploration in the stirred murk of the Well
(the copper helmet alone weighed thirty pounds, plus iron shoes
and lead necklaces), "I fancied that I was more
like a bubble than a man clogged by heavy weights"—and by the time
this observation from the realm of exotic and eminent
accomplishment is translated into my daily concerns, what
I see is a boy of five at his grandmother's bedside table,
where a bubble rises sluggishly up a glass of water
in which her teeth are parked for the night. They're not just
pink, they're the shockingly tropical pink of snorkeling
—coral and anemones—with thick discolorations
of a tetra-like canary, and he studies the homegrown comedy
and humiliation inherent in this object, as if rapt in front
of a sacred memento upfathomed from Atlantis itself. I

♆

know this: that the signs by which the universe exalts us,
shakes us like pig knuckles in a tin cup, parses, scorches,
and redeems us—these can be as small as a ticket stub,
as tacky as the fuzzy dice they shill at the carnival booths.
One summer night not long ago I clumped in line to ride
a risky upsytwisty thing they called The Boomerang. In front of me,
a couple—she was fifteen, maybe; he, a year more, tops. She
nursed an infant underneath her see-through blouse; its fuss
undid the scant deployment of the cloth enough so that
one lovely cinnamon-color shoulder was suddenly naked
to the midway wattage. And on it, in it, clearly: a love-bite
freshly reddening, every tooth defined. A fossil
of sexual passion, one school says. Another school: a fossil
of our foreknowledge of death, that sets us loving madly.

The Amounts

According to Franklin J. Foster of the University of Alabama, there are in existence about 200 pistols of which each owner believes he has the one that killed Abraham Lincoln.

Curtis D. MacDougall

As if there weren't enough. As if the 4,000 shoes
of Imelda Marcos packed like satiny roe in her closet
weren't enough, as if 300 species of the hummingbird
erasing clarity out of the still air weren't enough,
as if the secret names of God, and the wingéd skulls
on gravestones, and the total of the nocturnal emissions
of any night, and the stars in the night, and the sheer
and vexing twentieth-century info on neutrinos,
didn't anchor us in detailed texture enough. Oh,
and the Panamanian millipede with 784 legs.
The 4 million tons of bulk the sun loses per second.
And here's a sinuous Etruscan noblewoman reclining,
half-undraped, with bronze in her body (and so
a fake), as if the original (copper, tin, and trace lead)
weren't enough, as if the original Rembrandt beggar
with that vatic look on his candleglow face, or this
authentic Degas ballerina, as if the bedrock goddess
shaped in the cave mouth, fail but for called forth
duplication, sequels, xerox largesse.
1099: the sacking of Jerusalem brings back two
heads of St. John the Baptist. At least three churches
claim "the relic of Jesu's circumcision."

⊕

In the stories there are always six wandering brothers and
six imperiled, sequestered princesses. Three
wishes. Seven labors to perform. They start out once
upon a time, but of course the "once" is misleading,
the point is: singularity is something won through effort,
through enduring repetitive pattern, then
transcending it, to someplace out of the story.
Now he's sleepily reading the three-year-old to sleep
—a tale of Thumbling Henry nimbly overcoming,
one page each, "Ten Terrible Trials" (here
he's hitchhiking over the River of Doom on a turtle,
here he's spying on the no-goods from his hideout
in a hollowed ostrich egg, etc.); finally, with
the decagauntlet done, Hank wins the beauty's hand and
grows to full man-size—which on another night might
flicker some Freudian witticism through his mind but
this night, following bitter hours of bickering, the story serves
to say the fussy upkeeps of a marriage must be tended to,
the dooms and no-goods daily met head-on. He's
suddenly weak, with a remembered image of dailiness:
a bas-relief-rich pillar—around which, centuries
of pilgrims' individual kisses had worn a smooth ring.

Nothing is one thing. Sometimes the enormity
of that simple statement bonks him on the noggin with tweets
and zipping planets, just like in a cartoon. He sees
himself at the ever-mutating edge of the whole
Darwinian whelp it takes to be a *Homo sapiens,* his history
of brotherly consanguibeings, scaled
and nippled and webbed; he sees himself in partite,
every grainette and its infinitesimal chaff,
the atoms, the "sky" of atoms inside him, and
the emptiness inside *that,* and the "edge" of him
his wife might stroke, his rubber-gloved physician
lube and poke, but really the living skin is fumaroles
of give-and-take with every other singing, caterwauling
skin out there. Such skins . . . ! It's late and he's traded
the fairy tales for *Sensual: a catalog of intimate products.*
Who *are* these models?—slinkest they from what
genetic vat?—their skin like cream on fire, their wild and
cumulus blondeness . . .   Every minute, they're another world
than this one, where he looks in at the three-year-old and then
the thirty-three-year-old, his wife, in bed, with her own
unduplicatable web of connections . . .   There's a simple prayer
sane lives require: Let this one (*blank*) be sufficient.

Spaces

Beneath the Dome that afternoon, she studies reproductions
of Medieval and Renaissance paintings, with accompanying text.
In the former, Jesus, Mary, plus glorious saints and angels
bearing halos as solid and clearly-defined as hubcaps, all
appear against a flat, opaque (and often featureless)
background—in a sense, because this cast is more
important than the secular world, there is no secular world,
and they exist like figures painted on a wall, albeit
often a wall of gold and precious gems. But not much

later—say, the thirty years from Cimabue's Virgin
to Giotto's—scenes, like origami, open up.
By dozens of strategies that later will be codified
as "perspective," depth occurs: for the first time,
shadows; for the first time, railings running back,
with vases on them running back in recedingly smaller size;
and, for the first time, the deific is grounded in volume,
in an inventory: hounds and rabbits scamper
into "miles," into varicolored "distance" . . .   She

wills the neuro-vid to *off*. It's nearly dusk,
and through the Dome's translucent blueness
she can see the two moons sweep around
like snake-eyes in the sky. And then the Dome,
by planet law, opaques. It's Mars,
a thousand years from now. She sees the fiery trail
of the evening Earthbound rocket
scrape its orange on the deeply purple night, and thinks
how many ways there are

to conquer space. And now she stores the paintings' images
somewhere inside her mind—this mind
that they say is more interconnected than the universe
it's a part of—stores them
alongside her riled-up childhood days,
the man who hurt her once, the man who *she* hurts now,
the baby whose bawling is tugging her attention away,
the layered shames, the fears, the glow, the dream,
the death of that dream, then another dream, and another.

The One Thing

Now it seems a curious epoch in the history
of the human condition—lives were lines
reliably defining their limited contents,
lives were furrows turned by plow or
were a child-rearing space or were the rows
of barrels of salted cod, and discs of cheddar, and tea leaves . . .
and a marriage was seen as something further enlivening
this sameness, or if not marriage, then
"love," or "falling in love," an extra density
textured into the weave of the days, a craziness,
an orchidaceous interdimensional blossoming of the otherwise
linear creatures we were. The last gasp of this
long mode might be Hollywood's lush and screwball
sense of Romance; and a vestige of it

&

teases us now that the mode is reversed, our lives
don't have receptors enough for the fast, flashed
rollercoaster subatomic cybernetic funky input
of even a single twentyfour hours, and what
we want from love is reduction of this
to something accommodatable, as if
it were love's place to take incomprehensible knowledge
and make a maxim of it to live by. So:
the planet Mongo. There, intrepid explorers
Flash Gordon and company encounter
(in order) lion men, shark men, hawk men,
lizard men, tusk men, tree men, ape men,
often "stumble into their clutches," thus
are borne back to their dwelling places:

⚲

the lizard men's twisted communal cave,
the hawk men's spired aerial bubbledome city
floated high aloft by the power of "atom furnaces,"
etc. Physiognomy, psychology, armament,
casualwear—*everything* is ancillary
(even names: the ruler of the ice wastes is "Queen Fria")
to an overriding and clarifying original
singularity. Or the poem by Harry Mathews
(in his book *Armenian Papers*) about "brass islands," how
". . . their yellow wheat does not bend, and their peaks
Ring, flat . . .   Brass teeth, brass tears,
Brass breasts!" There's a city of living paper dolls
(so paper food and paper houses and a paper moon)
in one of the sequel Oz books, that a friend says

⨀

she remembers with a fondness close to painful,
on those days when the materials of her own life pile up
beyond assessing. And she says: the wars and I'm crazy,
the steady jackhammer racket of urban contempo music
and I'm crazy, today I'm supposed to be learning
the properties of electrolytic infusions and I'm crazy,
everyone is, we're here with a lottery ticket in one hand
and some NASA pix of Mars's brick-red surface in the other,
radon, alimony, one-day-sale, neutrino emission,
YOU BET I'm crazy, and then I come home, I
see he's crazy too, and I don't want the many-headed dragon,
I don't want the dancing goddess of countless arms,
I want the one thing, whatever it is, that's what I want and
what I've come to him for—the one thing.

Three Degrees of It

We're all arrived from off-planet.
I don't think that's an inaccurate description
of the amniotic sac.
It's not coincidental—aliens stranded on Earth
in countless sci-fi stories, waiting for the "mother ship"
to land and receive them back
into its opening belly. Being
alive at all, being human and being born of a human,
that commonest thing, is linked from the first
with a terrible strangeness. We're all from somewhere
farther than light.

℈

And once I asked a friend, a poet, the reason he
stayed in his hooker-and-stumbledrunk neighborhood;
he could leave, after all, if he wanted. "But—"
and then for a moment words failed him. We
were on the roof of his building. It was summer,
city summer, and the night air was heavy,
almost like a third person with us. "I want,"
and this was slow and meditative, "to be in community
with the wildness—you know? Not to give myself
over to it exactly, but . . . to know its pee's own scent.
To be its brother."

℈

A few blocks away is a basement club, and here
the wayward 17-year-old boy has brought his parents
to show them where, and with who,
he's been spending his time—intentionally to shock them.
Two men dance together: the nipples of one
are pierced by silver dollar–sized hoops. A woman
with a shaved head and a smoking gun tattooed on it
is singing—the backup band's actually pretty good.
His parents *do* think this is madness. You hear me?
They think *this* is madness. Meanwhile, the son is
keeping his lips shut tight: by secret patterns and clucks

he controls the entire room with his tongue.

Cheese

We know now it'll kill you.
Though they make a fake from vegetable oil
and zee it ("cheeze") so not to lie,
the real thing—what one old friend dubs
"dairy beer"—will clog the pipes
in opulence, and kill you. Yes, it's *that*
good. Cream uranium.
Even cheap ones melt luxuriously.
As gold, as rich, as a general's braid
or a Fabergé egg. Well, eggs will kill you.
The general's helped kill crowds of thousands.
Death'll kill you, and life'll kill you, and
all of us will be opened one day
found lined with a tincture of Muenster.

In Donald Hall's densely-textured paean "O Cheese"
—o sweet, or fungally musty; o white and upright
as a clerical collar, or peppery with the ambushed bite
of the mamba waiting inside—his subject is litanized
into an earthiness that glows: as if the magi
might have uncasketed *these,* for gifts as fit
as frankincense and myrrh, or even fitter, supposing
a god defined by birthslime
mingled equally with nimbus, and the close smells
of divinity and cow. They might be signs of exactly
that line where the body unbodies itself into something
beyond. In any case, I remember being a child,
a silly dumb Jew, and passing the church, and hearing
"Cheeses Love Me" winging into the clear high blue.

But the underside of a craggy saucer-sized fortress of
yesterday's cheddar is an exemplary study of entropy
and, possibly, simple offensive gunk. I've seen the maggots
overtumult like foam on an ale, out of an unpasteurized
wheel in Nice. "Toe cheese," my sister says, of our flesh's
own accumulation; "dick cheese" is another. "Who cut
the cheese?"—as if the body's sulfuric tuba is
never far in our minds from the pungency of a Brie.
Here's Mr. Dickens, describing a putrid room: "the walls
and roof of damp bare brick tapestried with
the tracks of snails and slugs . . .   the air was
sickening." So of course "it had been used
as a storehouse for cheeses"; he adds: "a circumstance
agreeably suggestive of rats."

♄

And "The other night at a college party / some students
told me that eating cheese / is when you eat a woman."*
Maybe that explains it: 7th grade, and we were touring
(wild little boogers that we were) the local Kist-Rite
Dairy Processing Plant. And if my heart went *ooga-ooga* over
Linda "Lovelips" Simon's nubbin nubility, in her
scraplet cling of a skirt—well, I was only one of seventeen
hormonal boy/men rapt at her each new cha-cha step
up the catwalk stairs. But it was Stevie Moskowitz who
angled so nobly far for a peek at The Goods, they needed
to rescue him, with clamorous interim drama, from a vat
of Swiss-in-the-making—gooped completely in it, rising
like a bad dream from its sticky matrix, scared
and gasping and staggering off and, I remember, *smiling.*

♄

---

*James Seay, in *The Light As They Found It*

When Morgan lived on public welfare, raising Dane
herself, the county food truck cornered up once a week
unloading a loaf "about as big as a couch or a coffin.
Now, the littlest whiff of anything similar, I'll start gagging."
It will follow us to the end. Those bitter contests
with my father, over a contraband dab of American
on *my* burger in *his* kosher home—the picky, pissy
battlegrounds love chooses! *It will lump in our eyes*
and our nostrils when we first break into light,
and it will follow us to the end. The day after
his funeral service I idly paged my "baby book," and in my mother's
scrupulous hand, I read "First Words": "*ba* (ball),
ca (car), *chee* (cheese)." It was there from the start.
It will tick like a time bomb in the ravenous singsong heart.

Fifty tiger penises destined for aphrodisiac use in France
were confiscated on June 5, 1991, at the Luxembourg border.
"I'm told," a customs official explained, "you grate them
on your food like cheese." But it needn't be so exotic.
Congregated, these are our brothers and sisters: as veined
as a fist of bleu, as blandly smiling as a family of farmer's.
The idiots (wouldn't Whitman say it "holy idiots"?)
dribbling from their rinds. The stalwart Cheshire,
the Gouda as smoky as a pillow saved
from a burning house. The rectitude of certain wedges;
others like fat pashas and their billowy odalisques.
The smearers, the crumbled, the shredded, the goat-funky ones.
The cheeses artificially flecked with dill or salami or chili speckles.
Humble cheeses, *chutzpah* cheeses, on-fire Greek saganaki.

⚛

And this is Linda Simon in her primmest (although it failed
at that) hand-tailored best. And Ava Becker, and "Choo-choo"
(really: that's all I remember) Tannenbaum. Here's all of the 7th-grade
raveables, and we who, whether brazen or craven, raved: Dick
Fleischer, Ronnie Mogel, Louie "the Bop Man" Nyeberg, oh yes
Stevie Moskowitz spiffily duded-up—there's thirty-six of us
plus Mrs. Stimpson our "homeroom" teacher, bleachered together
in three rows, all of us, ripening into the various zeniths
and deeps of that insatiable thing the future, all of us being
eaten alive by time that starts at our toes and won't give up
until it sucks the leastmost of the pang-bones and the whim-bones
and the woe-bones hollow, but *that* we don't know: *we're* fiiiine and
fierce and radiant. You know
what the photographer has us say.

Doctor Nitty-Gritty

1.

Albert's readers were probably less interested in his accounts of animal copulation than in his advice on human sex problems.

Herbert Wendt

The voices of friends in turmoil, over the voices of yesterday's friends
in yesterday's turmoil . . .   is a version of a palimpsest
(some days, of any two successive phone calls). If it isn't a life,
it's dying. Or it's—"heartquake," one friend calls it, with
its ancillary tremors in the brain and ('natch) the crotch.
Because we're mixed of gods and sewage, because we know it,
and because we don't know half enough, I have little to say

regarding the justly-famous three-hundred-ton butterfly
made of mating whales, breached completely free of their element,
belly to belly, delicately joindered at their sex; or of
the chalky daggers snails unsheath from their bodies,
repeatedly stabbing their partners; or of
the hummingbirds' stupendous courtship aerobatics
of 200 wingbeats *per second,* and of their cloacal love. No,

I would like this little candlelight to stammer on a human cadaver:
1306, Mondino of Bologna is—against the law, so wrapped
in a catacombed secrecy—dissecting a corpse: is slitting the major
entryways, then thimbling the humors and bloody pneuma,
upcoiling the vessels like angel-hair pasta, lifting each
new organ and its tissuey net of embellishments
with the wonder of a boy at a spilling piñata. You're my friends:

I don't want to wax morbid. But I'd like to ask you to keep him
in mind, tonight, when you approach your lover or
former lover or wannabe, I'd like you to think of me, in 1965,
in Phyllis Schneider's parents' sheetrocked basement, rising
thunderstruck and pussyrattled and sacred and scared
and triumphant: our own bodies, our amazing bodies, radiating
the five-alarm awe of The First Time. Maybe that

will be of some use. And if we did nip one another's yielded
shoulder-roll, like the sea lion or the marten; if
we licked, like the mouse, and the bat, and the relaxing
tensile jungle cat; if we lapped, if we howled, I tell you that
the animal *is* in it, that the pattern of ontogeny retains
the lizard and bird in our brains . . .   which surely is a version
of a palimpsest (some days, of any two successive emotions).

2.

Goldbarth . . . respects *feces, and takes an intelligent interest in them.*

Tom Disch, in a review in *Poetry*

Arnie, Arnie, women like to feel you respect them, roses,
private space, I'm saying to him, you know, like the Aretha
Franklin number. Later: *Rita, I'm telling her, all day Arnie*
lugs his ugly samples cases and pimps his own soul to shmuckolas
for you and the kids, he only needs a little show of respect
when he gets home trampled and spat on, you know, laugh
for chrissakes at his cornpone jokes. Such bullplop

fumaroles over the air, it does or doesn't do its gassy dab
of good, and then it's gone. Do I believe in it? One night
I remember when Ellen arrived home *mucho* drunk and vomited
(the gin having acted preservatively) a gout of perfect
three-course meal: every nubbin-headed broccoli floret, hoarded
whole against the acids; and I lifted one to the powdery
bedside light in what I see now was esteem

for the secret biocrenellations we carry inside us.
Or Ambroise Paré the barbersurgeon (circa 1560)
sees two soldiers, blinded, maimed, past any sane hope of recovery,
have gently had their throats slit by a comrade:
"I pray God, if I am ever in similar circumstances,
someone will be good enough to do for me what I
have just done for these two, sir." There is no muck

so low respect won't bend to meet it, and yes,
I would like to frankly consider the single hole of sex
and defecation in the platypus, *sans* comedy or aversion;
and the tiny pearlfish, parasitic, living in the rectum
of the baggy sea cucumber, lazily swimming in and out
"his anus for a door"; the various raisins and buttons; the great
Olympics discus of the ox; and the fecal pellets of molluscs, one

"a little oriental temple roof with its bottom edges turned
upward toward the sky" (Guy Murchie). I would simply like
Arnie returning, bouquet in hand, from a salesman's day
of eating it, of having to smile while eating it, of groveling
and licking his lips, and on the other side of his own home door
some magic scarab is being rubbed for its potency, and
from another twenty-four hours of mulch, a loveliness blossoms.

Fang

1.

They both remember the throat
is silver riverined
in the deep beet-color of blood,
a shockingly lovely expanse
the spent—the loser—wolf displays
below the aimed jaws of the victor wolf:
these two that have been battling
to the death, and yet now that the death
is a gift, an admission, the victor
turns from its completion, neurally-wired
for what the PBS narrator stops just short
of calling *pity* or *mercy*. He goes on to flashing
stills of a similar stimulus-sign in the violence
of baboons and other animals—zebras
was it? chimps? It's the throat of the wolf
they remember, the undeniable
persuasion of its flaunted susceptibility; that,
and how at this moment the three-year-old
came wringing the tears of a three-year-old
into the living room: he had peed,
it turned out, on the bigdeal heirloom rug,
and this announcement of the crime was
at once his protection.

2.

There's also a five- and also a seven-year-old.
She remembers it this way: every day
a three- and a five- and a seven-year-old, belovéd,
inescapable;
                they're nice all right, and funny, and you can watch them
rummage inside decision-making as if they were trying on grownups'
clothes, some suit that hangs like an elephant hide about them, but
mostly they're me-me-me and snotdribble, talking really *talking* to them
is like talking into one of those stupid fake cellular car phones people
use to look important, and anyway how can you say my children are
rapidly driving me with their endless savage opera of whoops like small
game to a cliff edge, how can you say this *to* your children, and yet who
else does she talk to outside of her nowhere job in Poop, Nebraska, well
her husband of course who she loves, and who's so even-keeled in
dealing with the nicked knee *and* the borrowed car *and* remembering
that when Nan and Oliver come for dinner Oliver can't eat shrimp so
let's do some of the fettucini plain just butter *and* who-really-hit-who-
first *and* even the tax deduction for Christ sake ALL AT THE SAME
TIME that she wants to make his penis smile as wide as a piano out of
pure appreciation and then immediately hates herself for always having
to play at The Appreciative One, not that he ever asks for that, of course
not it would be too imperfect, some days she could smash his face in
the press of the waffle iron, that's a good one, tell that to me-me-me for
a bedtime story, a three-year-old wouldn't believe it, surely her friends
her *thirty*-three-year-olds would shrug at her list of narcissistic bitching,
there are people being mangled under taxi wheels and raped with cheap
green bottles of wine by gang boys, who the hell is she to snivel about
this invisible little nibbling-away at her quickmeats, look it's nothing

even Vivian says her closest lady buddy, do you want a one-term membership at the workout club and we'll go shop for a lycra suit like mine with the matching sweatbands, look it's nothing.

But the bite of the wolf is something. The bite of the wolf can't be denied.

It's so simple: she makes of her wrist a throat. *". . . is silver riverined in the deep beet-color of blood."*

When he returns from the store he'll find her absentmindedly holding the razor.

There! (So simple . . .)

There! NOW *do you see?*

3.

Love cuts, his daddy told him once.
It's night, she's asleep, the bag of fettucini
is still where he dropped it.
      He remembers
it this way: every day, for everyone, needs stitching its imperiled seams
together every minute.

  Nan came over, after she'd heard. She was full of pronouncements. "*Everybody* has problems. Look, I have problems. Oliver's as crammed with them as an olive loaf. You can't take one woman's troubles and make a fetish of them." And there was more: the term "emotional blackmail" kept appearing. He had to ask her to leave—politely; she meant well.

  The grunge of it doesn't leave, however. He stares at himself in a polished spoon. He tries so *hard*. Well, they *all* try hard: he has to be fair. But some people's trying, let's face it, keeps a family a humming working unit. Some people's trying barely keeps *themselves* from blowing apart into pointillism. He feels very alone in Pit or Poot or Putt-Putt, Nebraska, as they call it. A smear in a cereal spoon.

  She really wanted to kill him and the kids, he knows, but loved them at the same time, to the same degree, and so she attempted its inverse. "This is a very creepy thought," he says to the spoon. And should he just beat the bloody shit out of her now, or seem as if he might, would that be cathartic? Should he simply go about the quiet tender ministrations of a worried caring husband? Yes, but wouldn't that very unruffledness and show of capability be an implicit rebuke to her recent hyperdrama? Mr. Spoon says, "It's a no-win situation." Once he hears it from an outside authority—Mr. Spoon is stern and impressive—he gets to say, without feeling guilty, "It isn't fair." Or anyway, without feeling *terribly* guilty.

He can see a line of civilized reaction (in a way, it's emblematic of what *makes* civilization possible) extending from the law of the pack to their own much-mortgaged shingle roof in Puke, Nebraska. Now the entire world has to stop and admire the glint of her razor blade and revolve around it.

... *now that the death is a gift, an admission* ...

You can't win against such weakness.

4.

Later that week, I visited.
I heard the story three times: his and hers
and theirs, which really makes three
different stories. The tv show
and the scatter of spinach pasta . . .   all of the details,
all of the pennyweights and bearings that keep
a great unthinkable thing from flying off.
They put the kids to bed, goodnight-goodnight-goodnight.
Then we could lose the public edge of ourselves
in a couple of bourbons—excellent stuff,
the kind with smoky ghosts inside—and talk with our individual
softnesses showing: the talk
of trusting friends. And then they took themselves to bed.
I was sleepless. This what I remember:
I wanted to gather them all in my arms;
but life doesn't work like the songs.
I wanted to write a poem that would heal;
but eventually we grow up, we learn about that.
So I just kicked around the guest room,
watching the night refold itself
over Putz or Pap, Nebraska,
a singularly opaque and enigmatic night.
I have to admit: I was useless there,
I was only a small slow bellows of sighs,
like some machine they'd left on, to humidify the room.
I walked out: the night was something enterable,
a black gas, something filming the face.
And then I heard it, and quickly returned inside,

I'd heard it licking its lips, I'd heard it
circling these friends of mine. And it wasn't only
this house on the plains, this clinical grief—no,
everywhere, I saw now, it was waiting for its chance,
wherever a door was open, any time a voice cracked.
It was born in the bones. It was burnt in the sky.
And the moon up there was an old old moon,
so slim and sharp, the oldest moon
that ever stabbed us
—the tooth of a wolf.

Life Is Happy,

I suddenly understand: I'm watching you chop away
at a cabbage, you're humming, the kitchen is light
and knife-thrust, light and knife-thrust,
lightslaw, airslaw, and humming. That would be the way
Life gets its blade out, then goes at it
with a human heart: maybe like somebody hacking
jungle undergrowth, so the whole heart's lost in a minute,
ribbons, pulp; or maybe making an exquisite show
of almond-like slivers, holding up
the fussy ricegrain-sized inscribings, studying
its artistry from many angles, taking years,
taking seventy years; but humming
in an absentminded, pleasurable way, no matter
the time involved, or what the technique—happy. This
was the lesson, now I remember, carried by the moted light
of the bulky, asthmatically-purring projector
they used for grade school "nature films." The room
was darkened, our tittering hushed, and then a voice,
a grave yet understanding, deeply male voice, came forth
from that machine, while on the screen a grainy lion
brought a grainy zebra down, and this was followed
by a few frames of its running with the bowel. This
was "the law of the jungle," "the law of fang and claw," and
so we understood that what we saw
as horrifying slaughter—and that zebra's widened jaws
and splayed gray teeth would bray inside my brain
for years—was part of a governing system, a balance:
there was pain, but it was ordered pain, and Life
was in the greenish jungle vapor, or the sky, all the while,
surveying its handiwork, calmly. Not *a life*, but Life
was happy, standing grandly in the kitchen

with its tools and its purview, neither king nor cabbage
more endeared to it, the knife out, at some moments
even looking like love, its hair, its hips,
its smooth, assumed efficiency,
its dearly off-key humming.

Entire Lives

If only the simple indigenes of the place disported themselves
in heathenish ways, and were like children, were degenerated
progeny of Adam, then it would be in the name of Christ that
they'd be made to work their fields for the Crown—and,
lo! they were, upon investigation, simple, and like children,
and denatured sons of Adam since Biblical days. How
well things work. How slyly beautifully the past
condones the moment. If only they this, if only
they that. If only my uncle touched me, here, and even
here, when I was young, if only my mother drank and
walloped me with the waffle iron, then you'd understand
I'm not responsible for this dangerous weather
storming around my head: the sudden floods, the falling rocks,
of getting to know me. In Victorian novels, narrative

☙

is the logic of causation: once
upon a time there was a violent rending of moral order.
An infant is abandoned in the dust mounds; or
two newborn babes are switched at birth; or one night
in the rookery an innocent serving-girl is seduced . . .
Whatever the wound, its stain appears 800 detailed pages later,
vengeances and curses and legacies shaping, in fact
explaining, entire lives. A friend of mine is up all night
in the 19th century, energetically touring its topiaried estates,
and the dike-workers' wattle huts in the marshlands, and
the gypsy camps, and the barristers' inner chambers . . .
There's some problem of a birthmark—though a problem
with an origin and a culmination, comforting
to that extent; exterior; nameable; blameable. But eventually the light

☾

of the 20th century, the late and frazzled drag-end of the century,
occludes the candles of Abbotshire and Chumley-in-the-Dingle, and
their place in an elaborate linkstitch pattern. Another
day of "real life" begins, and she faces into its pummel of unsolvable
mysteries. Is there a God? or no God? and in either instance how
    and why
are we here at all, and is there a Final Edge, and what's beyond it?
She sits at the window and watches the random drift
of the planet's dander winking in the weak and early sun.
What physics says is that we're elements (a little) mixed
in emptiness (a lot)—is it true? does it really describe
her hand she turns for study in this light, her hand
that's slapped a face, that's slept around a penis? is it
only densed-up air? is there a Purpose? are the lizard-selves
we once were still alive in us? . . .   That afternoon,

   ♄

in her therapist's office, several questions backtrack
to her childhood. A part of her is five and half-remembering
/ no, inventing / no, remembering / now there isn't any difference /
monstrous things. The part that's thirty-five blushes,
yes, then makes a momentary imagistic linkup
to a blush-red birthmark suddenly revealed
in a lawyer's rooms in Abbotshire: 800 busy pages
of deceptions and misapprehensions suddenly take regulated
shape, are given history, which is something like being given
a reason for having turned out this way at all. If only . . .
The therapist reaches into a mossy cavern . . .   reaches and,
lo!—into the tar and the bone-pit, into
the boggy deep . . .   Her uncle is moaning,
her mother is swinging the iron in its dark wonderful arc.

Stephen Hawking, Walking

*When I say that the orders "Bring me sugar" and "Bring me milk"
make sense, but not the combination "Milk me sugar," that does not
mean that the utterance of this combination has no effect.*
                                                        Wittgenstein

I rolled myself down to the Thames,
The better to ogle the dames
is a half-rhyme I wrote and like
and remember now at the riverside
where the molecules of my feet
inside my feet are very definitely arranged
in the act of walking; and,
whenever I think of those insubstantial tentacles
of subatomic particles from the gold skins of these women
—streaming out of them into the humid air that rests
as thick as a Guinness-head on the water, and from there out
to the ionosphere, in the evermix
of the universe—*then*
the molecules inside my feet are positively dancing,
oh and negatively dancing, and nothing
courtly either: the boogaloo or the dirty dog
from a honky-tonk in some American mill town!
I love the skins of these women and I want them

in the way in which we all want abstract beauty,
as when an equation clicks its tumblers into place.
I trust that some of them may want me in this same way,
though I see one walks an infant in a pram
who thinks my face is a deflated balloon.
My face is a deflated balloon
And looks just like a protozoon
is another jingly half-rhyme of my happy composition.
I want the baby's tears! The baby is sponsoring
two quick licks of salt out into this rivery air

that's as yellowish-gray as the keratin in horn.
I love the river, and *its* nonstationary skin. I want to lick
those saline runnels up those saucer-of-sweetcream cheeks
to the wet pink cinch of their being emitted! And
beyond that?—the consummate darkness
of the living human cavity! There is so much
left to love. No wonder my long work at the blackboard,
and the chalk, and the hundreds of thousands of seabottom corpses
comprising the chalk, and the puffed dust
winking around my logarithms and cosines,
make me want to lick these golden women

feverishly to the origin-spot, and then to the other,
impossible side of the origin-spot: because this is my
chosen labor, because the flowering cosmos necessarily
once was a seed, and I would enter it
doing whoop-de-do and the bossa nova. Someone
tether me to the planet, then let me
love the tether, chewing my way through its leather,
float me, squeeze me out endorphins from the ozone,
milk me sugar from out of the fleshes of the dancefloor couples
spinning themselves to a rose, and let me dwindle
into a tendril of motes in the first and the last,
the ur and the nano, the pixel and fiche,
the sexual and celestial singularity of everything
the universe imagines through *us*,
its language. This

I've needed to tell you in words, though
in the molecules inside my head
I've thought it completely in numbers.

Acquisitions

The museum's newest, tooted in the media even down to a what
to name them competition for the kids (where Scooter & Skeeter are
    so far
favored) is a pair of flying waterfowl an Ice Age artist carved
in ivory so abstractly it takes a blink to see this stylized
cross or dagger is really a sleekly avian glide, and
then your breath catches. The city's glitziest connoisseurs
and tv news were gathered here when, who knows why,
a young street artist snapped, began a dance somewhere between
kabuki and epilepsy, and *very* quickly was roughhoused out
of the gallery, back to the street, and from there to another museum
of sorts, the City Asylum. I'll return to the ivory birds but
not before we watch him being stripped of everything,

his clothes, his name—he spends a week unpersoned this way,
then the following morning they find he's written SHIT
with his own, across the rec room wall in letters two-feet tall,
it being his only possession and, to that extent, the whole
of his increasing need to individuate himself
(although they'll only understand it as one further stage of the madness).
Other inmates save their fingernails in tiny caches hollowed
out of the soaps, or build up balls of the dirt from under their nails
—nothing stops our urge to say this beautiful thing
is mine. Those striking tannin-color ivory flyers
the p.r. staff is so gaga over, are carbon-dated to such a dizzying
point B.C., I wonder were they functional

(the keys, let's say, that opened winter's iced-up locks;
or tally markers; or small hellos to the god)
or did these enter through that nano-door in history
where someone simply wanted his or her own life
embountied by the loveliness of owned and otherwise
wholly gratuitous objects? If not these ivory birds,
these scored bone buttons. If not these buttons, this plaque.
As soon as burials appear in the strata,
there's grave goods. Here's the photo of the skeleton of one
Cro-Magnon man, still in a headband strung from fox teeth,
wearing garlands of beads as fatly swagged
as these overpacked, orotund stanzas of mine.

♄

I'll write with the strict, and yet-mild-tempered, reserve
of Elizabeth Bishop. I'll write with the loony encompass
of Kenneth Koch. I'll revile this war and all wars and their
retrospecies makers; and I'll praise the teeming details
of my purview, from the fires-stippled night sky, to the little
kitschy quiddities by which my day is lightened—like this 1937
Ungle Wiggily board game, mighty fine an item even fifty-four
years later: Ungle Wiggily Longears suffers from "the rheumatiz" and
only your plucky throws of the dice can safely maneuver this
sympathetic rabbit gent past perils like the awful shears-beaked
Skeeziks, to the ministrations, far in the upper-right corner,
of Doctor Possum. The museum tells us this is nothing

new: toy rams and chariots have been raised from the rubble
of Sumer; or from ancient (circa 1300 B.C.) Egypt, here's
a board game, *senet*, of acacia and faience, all
of its wood tokens and knucklebone dice: intact. It's easy
enough to see two soldiers sliding the hours away with this,
in the lull of a shitty campaign. And then the horn sounds, and
in the snap of a finger they're two lopped necks on a battleground.
Update it to poker and fighter jets, and nothing's really changed;
for some, "acquiring" means nation-states—the very urge
I'm writing this about, but on a monstrous scale, making
human Skeezikses of everyone it touches. I say: keep it
small. Those ivory birds: exquisite spirit-thumping things, but

small, a flock could fit in your pocket. Of course we know
someone who isn't allowed to have pockets. In fact he
isn't allowed to use the ward's one toilet himself,
not after the wall-smearing scene: they
make a bored attendant stand there, watch him wipe, and wait
until he flushes. And at night, in the isolation cell,
when he's strapped to his pallet and finally alone, "Eyesaiah" comes
to visit. It's a pun he's invented, a Biblical-sounding name
for when he closes his eyes. He sees his friend
in the shape of one of those Ice Age birds. It circles,
then lands . . .   The darkness under those two closed wings
is the one thing they can't take away from him.

Engravings in the Books of the 17th-Century Scientist/Mystic Athanasius Kircher
(with an epigraph from a video catalogue)

*This award-winning film . . . goes to the very edges of the universe,
then back to Earth and into a human hand, ending up inside a proton
of a carbon atom.*

Beryllium is there. Styrofoam is there. The circuitry
of the gamete, and the shed blood of the warring hosts,
and the plastic Monopoly buildings, and the jellyfish-dangle
effluxion of ghosts . . .   I mean the edge of the universe,
the nacre of the mind of God, the very birth-spot of Fire,
the Ice of the North, and Nothing—even Nothing:

everything is there; and departs; and returns; and is mixed
(inert, or alive in its shine and its ribosomes,
depending); and is remixed; and appears, then,
in our vale of transient human aspirations. Undepictable,
of course; and yet engravings in the books of Athanasius Kircher
try: The Lord, or His Son, or one of the Muses is seated

centrally in so many of them, and the Formative Powers
of Life as We Know It symmetrically radiate outward: the Tree
of the Seven Planets (each with corresponding masterangel),
the Signs of the Zodiac, every beam of Universal Magnetism
from the 72 names of God Himself, to the flickering worldly
knowledge of, say, Pythagoras or the Pharaohs . . .   But

♄

I like best an illustration for his *Arca Noë*: simply
forty-three laborers building that vessel according to client Noah's
Yahweh-specific blueprint. They mallet, they buttress, they translate
the directive from On High into the terms of down here:
increment; sweat; and the constant need for repair.
The engraver has given their arms the bell-like swells

of construction workers any-where or -time, and
a few of them bend to their various poundings as if banging it
straight and true might be a matter of importance beyond
the day's wage. "Shit," one says. Another whistles. One is thinking
of pussy, one of saving those shavings of cedar and making
a doll for his sick girl. None especially seems deserving

of destruction. Do they understand they're hewing and nailing
        and trimming
a salvation that's denied them? Ninety-eight of these pages
later, there's another illustration: people kneeling on the rocks
are reaching piteously to those in the water, the rising water.
Some hands meet; some fail to meet—these hands so good
with wood and caulking. From here, they might as well be

&

—well, *here*: a corner bar called Hammered and a moil of people
between the late shift and home. They're drinking away
one more long day's shortcomings, and I don't see why
atonement is an applicable concept, what redemption has to do
     with this
small laundering in beer-suds of what's soiled in us
—call it the spirit, call it the guts. Out back, a man

in oily leather is pestering a woman, first
with words and then with clumsy, almost tenderly clumsy,
mauls. A man in denim steps in. They fight,
the man in leather falls, and such is the honeycomb intricacy
of humankind, that the woman crumples weeping theatrically
over him, cursing her denim protector: it was none of his

fucking business, it turns out. Later, I see her in the parking lot,
alone, and staring wonderingly at her open palm. Not because it's hurt
or stained, but staring at it: her hand neutrinos shoot through,
her hand composed of the same mandala of sub-sub-elements
as the hearts of stars—just holding it up to their light
and asking the gods she knows, what's the deal.

Little, Big

Words I'd like to get in a poem,
hemoglobin and chifforobe and ombudsman and mahogany.
Meanwhile, a friend is studying the *mahāyuga*,
the "Cycle of Cycles," 4,320,000 years,
and its relationship to subvibrations of charm
or salsa or stodginess or whatever other
qualities are being ascribed this afternoon to the spectral
stipples of quantum physics. Another friend is formidably
gaga over cetology, and if she could would happily spelunk
the living gullet with rope and calipers; the penis
is prodigiously ten feet, their underocean songs
unscroll a hundred miles, etc. And here I am,
with seiche, chignon, persnickety, with hobnob,
allemande, fandango, and grommet. Here we all are,

mostly, cleaning the pleats of our fussy little pursuits,
our ball bearings and milk teeth; banging spear
on horsehide shield, against the residue
kablooey of the Big Bang; gung-ho throwing our bodies
into love, our bodies that are jackstraws
cast by gods in games of chance. Inside
such vastitude, our harvested ambitions pop
like corn and are gone in an instant. Either that, or by
their brevity, and a passionate care we lavish on this brevity,
they take on their peculiar human beauty. When I
stayed with my cetologist friend, I saw her bed,
a box spring cleanly joindered to a frame of varnished
whale ribs; so she and her husband dreamed
and clutched in a basket of those colossi. Late

♄

that night, I pass their door: I'm thinking fritz
and blitz and scalawag and leukocyte but stop
at sex's tremolo (she'd have her fist of hair unpinned,
outfanned; and he'd be lost inside her rhythm . . .);
or it's sobbing. *Rumor*, is that what I hear? or *tumor*?
—one more pointillistic jitterdot
by which a life for better or worse is transported.
I walk out on the deck in a cloud of the small words,
photon, muon, leprechaun. I know that somewhere
a man paints faithful portraits of friends on grains of rice.
I know that out on the waters tonight, the whales slide
together like hands in prayer the size of city blocks.
And gently, almost powdering it, the ombudsman moon
ameliorates the naked light of the sun.

A Slightly Shuffled History of Western Civilization, with Three Moons

Sir Francis Bacon. He actually died because he caught a chill going out and gathering snow to see if it would preserve a chicken. . . . So I tried to write a poem about that. Then I tried to write a poem about landing on Mars.

Pattiann Rogers, in an interview

That night the snow fell as if prototype gears
for all of the planet's clockworks had been loosed
from Heaven, each flake was that complete and individual
in the malt-colored light of the moon. And then
"he was taking the aire in a Coach with Dr Witherborne"
and ordered it halt at a poorwoman's hovel, "and
bought a Hen, and made the woman extenerate it," the gut
scooped out as smoothly as a child's picked nose. And
then? The plague. The Boston Tea Party. We walked
on the moon. My father said "Here—" and pretended
he grabbed a snowflake from the atoms of the night, and
set it, solid as a casino chip, on my tongue. He
told me each was like a Jewish star: six points.
He taught me knotting my tie, the Windsor and
the four-in-hand, the tell-all silky dimple. And
then? The prom. Vietnam. The singular compulsions
of ink and testosterone. When Francis Bacon "wrote," he
dictated, pacing "in his delicate groves";
Thomas Hobbes was only one of many amanuenses.
Bacon working out a theory of atoms. Bacon
constructing a "weather glass." The quaint and
honorific light by which we see the legendary dead.
My grandmother—Nettie, in her gray braids,
matter-of-factly yanking the whole connected mess
from the chicken, not much more
than chicken-sized herself. She sang, she stitched,

she soiled her adult "safetee pants" and the brocade chair.
And then? He wept when the rabbi nasally wailed
her name in Yiddish, all that season he wept.
He tried to explain it—I was 13—but
death is no knot's simply coming undone. I
fretted, I dreamed of the buttery vee
of Maria Alfonso's cleavage, I read: how Dürer
died from sailing to see a beached whale
"in Zeeland." Bacon died of snow
he molded into the rank pursed-open bowelcase.
Then I tried to write a poem: ". . . snow fell
as if the prototype gears for all of the planet's clockworks . . ."
—baloney, it seems to me now. When Bacon wrote,
he shared that map—it was the landing of his mind's flights—
with the likes of George Herbert, Ben Jonson,
and William Harvey. Maybe Herbert showed him
"Easter Wings." Harvey with a sharpened grouse quill
lilting up the burred serifs and exes
of his sketch of the circulation. And then? This
war, that war, a few gods and some annexed countries,
the car and the cartoon. And then. That fraudulent
"and then." *I wish events to be* (such sweet intention!)
coupled with their causes—Bacon.
The smell of "neates leather" offended him. He had
"a delicate, lively, hazel Eie—like the Eie of a viper."
He rode in an open coach "when it rayned," imbibing
what he called *the Universall Spirit of the World*.
And then? Ague. He couldn't even stomach a final
draught of March-beer. He left behind *The New Atlantis* and
22,000 pounds in debts. He tried to explain
the infinitesimal ties between one life and another. And
then. One day my father died. "Here,"
he said when I visited him on the other side
of the grave—and his hand
swept over the canals as if exhibiting his personal
engineering skills, and the red red dunes,
and the polar caps, and the oystershell moons.

Us / Claudia / Talleyrand

The hyperreactive yammer of the neighbor's car alarm
has sprung you up in bed with the frizzled
and mad-eyed look of a Biblical prophetess, cursing,
cursing. But I'm wakeful-eyed beside you
already—the idiot, lyrical gossip of a few June birds
having been enough to rouse me. Am I more

"sensitive" to extraneous sound than you? Well first
define "sensitive." Suddenly both of us are, to the thought
that we might not be. I knew a woman once who
claimed she was so sensitive in her anyway wholly
luscious skin, that she could patter from bed and be
more chilled by stepping bare-soled on the silver

shine of a dime than on the duller copper surface
of a penny. But I quickly see that resurrecting her
into our conversation, allowing her even a single
photon of the limelight, is an idea that ranks approximately
around genocide on a list of tasteful subjects. Sensitive
sensitive sensitive. Talk talk talk. "A man like me

cares little for the lives of a million men"—Napoleon
Bonaparte. In fact over two million people died
directly as a result of his campaigns, with countless others
dead of attendant miseries; 17-year-olds by the thousands
were simply ordered breast-ahead into the line
of enemy fire. In this climate, Talleyrand

thrived—*representing* that climate, as Foreign Minister; a man
"mercenary, worldly, mendacious, treacherous and
without scruples" (Paul Johnson). And yet at the Vienna Congress
Talleyrand arrived with "one of Joseph Haydn's pupils
. . . to play the piano softly—background music, hours at a time—
while he worked at his desk." The definition of "sensitive"

veers away, reconstitutes, is just as much the blood-sense
of a shark as it is a butterfly, and utterly fuddles our morning.
In any case, it's all we can do, to kiss, and stretch,
and enter our separate days of gumption and money,
girt in our separate appropriate battlegear. *Some* days
nothing perturbs us, such is our threshold. Other days . . .

that car alarm. They say it's
so *exquisitely* overstrung, what sets it jangling is
the droppings of those few June birds.

The Counterfeit Earth!

1. Ballpoint C & C

It's 2157. Two adventuring spacemen rocketing home
are stupefied by a vision of side-by-side twin Earths
—one (which one?) being a "mega-televised mock-up"
concocted by wily Terran scientists as proof against
a rapidly approaching alien warfleet: if their test ship comes
within 1,000 miles of the duplicate planet, hidden
"atomic batteries" will fry it with a bolt and,
chain-reactioning, will fry the entire enemy armada.
Fine. But what about our heroes, caught in space
and facing the same impossible choice, huh? Well,

    ♄

it's 1963. I close that comic book. I'm 15: there
are realer pressures. I'm in a men's-room stall and scrawling
ballpoint cocks and cunts (these loopy doodles are miles
away from being "penises" or "vaginas") on the already
much-cocked sheetrock. Is it criminal
defacing? is it primal confrontation with The Great
and Sacred Mysteries? etc.—I'll get to that. For
now, it's one more 15-year-old man/boy overbrimmed
with the whelm of daily life, and venting it, quickly, in language
as old as the first flame-licked cave walls. It's

    ♄

79 A.D. This same symmetrical, cilia-rayed, puffed pout
and roughly bulbous protrusion are being scratched
on the wine-house walls of Pompeii. Amid the archwayed
garden-walks of the gentry, these appear. Around
the laurel-bordered frescoes of the gods, and on the altar bases,
these are drawn, and plastered over, and redrawn.
Outside the Temple of Isis, and there in a farther corner
of the Villa of Papyrus Scrolls, while hair is coiffed,
and wax tablets are smoothed, and the suckling pig is spitted . . .
A skull. Wings. Labia. Ass cheeks. Lightning. Erections.

2. Survey of Types

Now that graffiti *is* art, and wins its fellowships
and coffee-table books and tv interviews like any art, we
might want to remember its first appearance *in* art, in
Giacomo Balla's 1902 oil on canvas, *Bankruptcy*,
a close-up of two massive wooden panels of a doorway
so long unused, they've become a museum of chalk
streetscribbling: gutterscribbling really, it's so
crudely splenetic, so schematized an explosion
of bawdy comedy, despair, and rage, so willing to place its
dignity in chalk used like a tripe-plucking knife

☮

—not a "counterfeit," no, but a *counterweight*, Earth
that balances the galleries of oil portraits of merchant princes
and dandily pampered nudes, and came before. Now where
to draw the line between such raw, guerrilla lines and
the equally raw and yet grandly pictoreligious scratchwork
unto The Mother Goddess or The Priapic Shaman, in Ice Age
stick-and-circle art we've trained our later eyes to see
as devotional? We never know; the lines behind the fierce, illicit
scribbles of the Balla painting, Dickens understood: the deprived,
the sellers of their own children, the feral, the hunted-down

☮

—yet turn the nearest corner, and these on-the-lam inscriptions
are a randy celebration, flanked by a joyful crayoned fireworks
and an inky goatee on the chin of a famous cabaret chanteuse.
Perhaps all we can say of them is what *they* say, always,
under what they say: "I'm here, my peck of elements is charged
        and cohering,
I make things." In Greece, at Sunium, at the temple of Poseidon,
Dr. Edward Dodwell slept in a cavern, sketching the view,
examining the columns both toppled and standing. Rose Macauley
writes: "Did Dodwell carve his name? Nine years later,
Byron, of course, did so." Whistling. Nonchalant. Of course.

3. From Somewhere Beyond the Moon

And Dickens visited Pompeii, saw the stone jots
of its stopped-watch life, "the chafing of the bucket-rope
in the stone rim of the well, the marks of drinking-vessels
on the stone counter of the wineshop . . ."   A soldier's just
paid for his red that, somewhere between the amphora
and his cup, gets watered. But what the hell. The mountain's a little
angry today, but what the hell with that too. This
afternoon he's lush with feeling as much as with drink,
and on his way home lifts his marking-stone and,
at a back but very public wall, unlooses:

     ⚘

this same set of cartoon genitalia our 15-year-old does,
while the earliest States-release of the Beatles *yeah-yeah-yeahs*
through the bar-&-grill air. I remember that boy so well,
his openness to moil and flux . . .   Bob Dylan nasally singing
"The Times They Are A-Changin'" can bring him to his knees
(when he's alone in his room) with emotion from somewhere
beyond the moon. Or so can something he and his friends have learned
to call "injustice." And as for the milky, silky cling
to Laura Maggowicz's ass-cleft as she passes in the hall . . . !
It's all too much. By now he's home for the night, and reopens:

     ⚘

this, his nickel-bin (thus coverless) copy of
Mystery in Space (for January 1957) which he completes
before sleep pulls him into its own enormous darkness and stars.
Our goodguy rocketeers, it turns out, touch down surely
on the real Earth, but simulate exploding, with jolts of energy
channeled off their engine. Wholly flimflammed, the waiting aliens
zero-in on the *other* planet, and consequently get flashed
into atomic cinders: happy ending, goodnight. Oh, and how
did our heroes know?—well, only the real Earth showed "the Great
Wall of China, which can be seen from space." So

Zen: the writing *is* the wall.

12,000 Bones of Frogs and Toads

1.

You have to believe what's there. It's all there is.

And there's another line I've always liked in that poem
by William Carpenter: ". . . *a book*
can make sense of a human life." Yes, that
I believe. I say it. I say it so often I think
I wrote it. I repeat it
in the light of noon, that zags off traffic's fenders
like a raygun fight, in a sci-fi movie, and
I repeat it at night, in the quiet, here,
the minds of my neighbors become as unthinkably
distant as Mars's umlaut moons.
If I say it a minute longer I'll wear it
into meaninglessness, pure mantra-fizz, some figurine
rubbed lovingly smooth of the detail it was loved for.
Yes, *a book . . .   a life . . .*   I say it as if rehearsing
for its moment of need, like CPR. And
even so, when the phone explodes
at my bedside at horribly 4 in the morning
—the friend grenade—
and Barbara's "not sure *where* my life is going"
and the pieces of that antiknowledge float us both
to the rims of ourselves,
where the view out is a landscape of chance
so dizzying, there isn't any reason

I have nothing
to say. If there's a book
its text is foreign. If there's a book
its language is dandelion chaff.

2.

In the ages of faith, people believed that . . . everything meant something. Every possible article in the world, and its name also, concealed a hidden message . . .

T. H. White, *The Bestiary*

And so the Panther, of the "variegated colour,"
is Christ, "of so many colours
that he is the Apprehensible Spirit, the Only Wise,
the Manifold, the True, the Sweet, the Suitable,
the All-Seeing." And, if you "accept in your ear
the seed of God's word, but put it away in the wrong place,"
you are like unto the Weasel, "for some say
they conceive through the ear and give birth through the mouth."
The Crow means love of children. The Hedgehog,
prudence. Even stones: *the mightie yron, Fortitude; Virginitie,*
the ruby. Real whales, real worms, are words
defining an abstraction. Any oblong
of the world an open door defines, is open
encyclopediacally—and a man will exit,
labor, and return
to sleep at the end of a day of each
least sliver of cedarwood, each cattle louse,
instructing him.
                    And the man who wakes
illiterate to this . . . ? Who hangs up wearily
from Barbara but keeps on calling himself
with impossible questions, falling

into jittersleep, and thinly at that, an hour . . .
For him, the text of the planet will be an unrosetta'd
pictographic squirm . . .   I
                                        blearily stare
at the bleary-eyed stare in my mirror, pressing
slow and resolutely at the bone beneath my face, just
to be sure of something. Maybe
a statement of destiny really is
encoded grainily in fish skin, in the script
a peach pit mazes over its surfaces,
maybe all of the moral virtues, and a strength whereby
to incorporate them, and the luminous
faces of Glory, are doodled
casually but clearly in the veining of anything
grown from this Earth—maybe,
if only we'd recognize them.
                                        Hawthorne's
note toward a story:
"Some moderns to build a fire on Ararat
with the remnants of the Ark."

3.

*Archaeologists had even named some [Paleolithic people]. There was
the Frogman of Veyrier, found near Lake Geneva with 12,000 bones
of frogs and toads . . .*
John J. Putnam, article in National Geographic

And "the Petersfels children" are so named,
who were found in their West German forest
"with fox paw bones." "Romito 2," a dwarf,
"from a cave in the Calabria region of Italy."
—That's it; the rest is decontextual
murk, the fox paw bones "suggesting fur wraps,"
but we'll never *know.*
                    And Barbara the Friend
—the name means what, and who is she? Don't
ask *her* tonight: the pop-psych phrase
"identity crisis" floats on a darkness
older than she is; one by one
the letters of her name slip off her self and
bobble over the horizon . . .   I can feel
my own name tugging. And you . . . ?
—you'd better hold hard to yours.
                            Tonight,
who's anyone? For instance: here
are color cibachrome photos of happy wisecracking tourists
at Nazi death camps forty years after,
taken by photographer James Friedman
—they lounge at the outdoor café with a Bass Ale awning,

that overlooks an "execution area"; the grass
gets mowed as in any national park;
nearby the basement room
where "a human dissection table" is still intact,
a cola delivery truck purrs up to a concession stand . . .
There are distances here more vast
than in that sci-fi movie, where intergalactic
adventurers return to Earth from hyperdrive in light-years,
and their greatgreatgreatgreatgrandchildren greet them
unintelligibly. I have cousins
whose names are forgotten, burnt to ash and buried
in West Germany not far in either lateral *or* horizontal distance
from those Paleolithic children who appear
named in the archeological literature,
                              and
what does it mean, and no wonder we dial
the people we care for and ask who we are. Tonight,
with sleep a worn-through one-ply mental layer
anyway, I'm going to wait for the sunrise
by saying the names of my friends and
asking you to say them and adding your own if you'd like,
yes Barbara, and David, and Jimbo, and Jeanmarie . . .
whose lives are messages we need to tell each other
count, whose bodies are books of beautiful
calcium litanies: the crazy bone,

the sanity bone, the fletched sexbone in its ecstasy bullseye,
the meatgrinder bones, the thumping warchief pestle-bone,
the joy bone, the woe bone, the midden-dump bones
in the memory centers, the sweet bone, the salt bone,
the dwindling frog bone corridor of our ontogeny,
the bone bridge back to the bone germ plasm,
the *ur*-bone,
the babysbreath bones of the soul.

The Way the Novel Functions

In the s-f story you read then dream, a person is
an inch. And so a flower is a monstrous thing,
an insect monstrous more. Out rooting, Unkh
and Titi-bara and seven others of the Tribe were caught defenseless
in the open by a Tiger Wasp—and eight were never found but
Tuska's body was, injected with that waxy stuff
the wasplings eat on hatching: nobody would touch it now,
it wasn't fit for proper Tribal burial and, from the sun,
it swelled to deep sebaceous-yellow in a day.
There's also pleasure here: the wedding night is ritually spent
in a full-blown rose, the couple tussling in that overfolded
tissuey embrace; or simply keeping watch by night,
the ring of fires making ingots of the acorn husks
the rest of the Tribe curls sleeping in . . .   Though
mainly it's fear, it's guardedness and fear, it's every minute
under attack. The Hornets will dive in a pack or by ones.
The Mantis is three-men tall but blends in all too greenly.
It will devour a child with horrible motions of etiquette,
its leg can be used for a saw. And at night, the armor-plated
Stalker Beetles, heavy, yet so quick, their jaws
can slice a throat like aspic. One is breaking
through the slats right now, is gripping you . . .   You
wake. It's day. It's only a day. It's only the common
enormous day to get through, the day with its six
invisible legs and its feelers, the day on your chest.

Effect over Distance

The six-foot indigo plumes of "the sacred necropolis bird
of ancient Egypt" rose from urns on either side of the stage,
and there were billows of an inky incense just as thick . . .
Amaz-O the Grandiloquent, "beguiler of both royalty and the masses,
from the steppes of Outer Shaz to the salons of naughty Paree,"
was about to flabbergast the annual convening
of the Synagogue Social Society for the northwest side of Chicago,
in 1960, when I was twelve, and embarrassed of being twelve,
and embarrassed of my parents, who sat on my either side
like the upright plumes of the squarest, drabbest avian life imaginable.
He'd already been successful at scarves and rabbits
and an unbroken river of golden hoops—"And NOW,
I shall endeavor to READ THE MIND of an audience member
across this Emptiness Between Us!" I was sick with fright
then, feverish and clammy at once; for I knew I'd been thinking
of his slinkily-spangled assistant in her barely-there sarong
and snakey boots, and she reminded me, by easy links
in logic, of Miss Portney, assigner of *Ivanhoe* and *Silas Marner*,
whose tailored-over swells and winky fissures had me
imagining voluptuary excesses that were poignantly real
if (given my inexperience) sappily vague, and might be best
summed up by picturing the wallowing of a seal in sweetcream.
I knew—he was going to probe this rotten nethermind
of mine, and though he'd be too gentlemanly
to reveal my moral putrescence in public, still,
it was inevitable some tincture of his discovery, some
greenish O of weeks-old eggs, would float the air above
and give my budding culpability away, to these
assembled hosts of goodness. If it seems foolish now,
that fancy, I take comfort from the instances of similar belief
in dramatic effect taking place

across impossible distance, sometimes instances believed in
by the wisest and the most. We know Medieval scholars
placed their faith unquestioningly in "green vitriol." Listen:
"If a piece of a wounded man's raiment, stained with blood
from the wound, be dipped in water holding some of this
miraculous powder in solution, the wound forthwith begins
to heal. It matters not how far the sufferer is away
from the place where the blood-stained scrap is treated.
The patient might be in affliction in Marseilles,
and the piece of linen might be effectually operated on
in London." Of course. Even now, in travel, I'll suddenly
think of my wife back home, and know whatever
love or shame, whatever tangled fear or passion, is the major thread
of that etheric fabric—weaves a visible pattern
of cause-and-effect in the actual world. In 1728
the obdurate, carpenter father of novice astronomer
Thomas Wright of Durham, England, gathered and burned
the fledgling scholar's books; well, I know perfectly how
that conflagration smoldered over twenty-two years, eventually
becoming his pioneering vision of swarms of suns,
of flaming uncountable bodies, scattered
throughout "the endless Immensity." By the way,
Amaz-O read the mind of a tittering corpulent woman
named Minnie Pinkus, who must have been putty inside his
well-kept prestidigitorial hands—it was a matter of missing car keys,
furtively-eaten extra desserts, and some implied
erotic transgression so insipid the audience needed to *will*
its fitful blush and laughter to the surface. She sagged back
into her seat aswim in sweat. So I was spared,
I guess, although those very easy links of logic fastened me
inseparably to Thomas Wright—for even once
we'd moved on to the floating globe, and the pocketed fish,
I sat there on fire, I sat there burning into the starry future.

The Emergence of Flight
from Aristotle's Mud

You bitch, you sonofabitch, you flaming bitch-on-wheels . . .
This rancor, where it comes from, what the seed is
of these writhing eels bollixed in the human breast,
we can't determine, any more than Aristotle himself
saw past the fallacy of surface: ". . . and so eels
and others are generated spontaneously—from 'earth guts',"
or from horses' hairs spaghetti-like in water. Frogs sprang,
green and grown, from river soil. Tapeworms spiraled
alive from the slough of our own guts. Maggots
slathered up out of a pregnant cheese. How many

hundreds of struggling, blind-hunch years before
Malpighi attempts to artificially fertilize the eggs
of an opened silkworm; or Maria Sibylla Merian
faithfully follows, and faithfully draws, the mysterious
progress egg-to-caterpillar-to-pupa-to-butterfly!
For us, meanwhile, breakfast is a war zone,
for the sake of sleep the bed is a limited armistice,
you cunt, you asshole—even our sweetest creases used
as armament—and what engenders this bitterness
suddenly out of love is so unknown I call it "Aristotle's mud."

⌐

This is the same unknowing behind the skirmishes
of nation-states, of chosen versus infidel, but I prefer
more individual focus. Benvenuto Cellini is traveling home
to Florence; one night as his weary party considers an inn,
the host insists on payment in advance. "I did not get
one wink of sleep, in thinking how best to revenge myself.
At one time it came into my head to set fire
to his house; at another, to cut the throats
of four fine horses he had in his stable." (Cellini
weenily opts for slitting the beds on departure.) Or

in 1779, in San Gennaro, Naples, Michael Kelly
goes to the cathedral to witness the miracle
when the congealed blood of Saint Gennaro liquefies:
"then the Te Deum is sung, and the whole congregation
prostrate themselves with devotion, and every face beams
in delight." One time the obdurate phial of blood
refuses its on-command transforming. "The old ladies
particularly cried out 'You yellow-faced dog!'
'Cursed rascal!' and" (easily my favorite)
"'Porco di St Gennaro!'—'You pig of a Saint!'"

One day—I was 13, a willful if noodley man/child—
I simply said no: I didn't believe in that overblown fiction,
God; I wasn't going to carry the torch of ritual observation
one more theostifling day. You might think, 31 years
later, I'd remember that flash of pintsized liberation
with a secret smile and thrill; but what I remember is . . .
You know how, in a dream sometimes, events are seen
in overlay, or urgency allows us the briefest,
inspired, composite vision?—I could see my father's
heart break, in his face. And even that

wasn't enough, no, not in the throes
of hyperspite. I snatched the *yarmulke* off his head
—his skullcap, his cherished—and flung it,
with a shabby self-conscious insouciance, into Chicago's breeze.
My reasons?—whatever I thought they were, they
weren't. Whatever it finally meant to knowingly sketch
the live moiré of a butterfly, to squeeze the silkworm egg case
of its infinitesimal contents . . .   There I was, staring
stupidly after it as it fluttered, rose, and was lost
to sight: its sky-blue silk in the blue of the sky.

The Dating Report

Don calls, to tell me about a woman he's dating.
He likes her—though her psychic therapist says she

drowned in Atlantis. "So many small things push us apart."
His tightass opinion of television . . .   her kids . . .

the first cracks in the city ramparts . . .   panic . . .
grabbing up coins and some earrings . . .

the waters pouring in between.

Arguing Bartusiak

Space-time simply doesn't exist where loop lines are absent, any
more than a blanket exists between the weave of its threads.
                              Marcia Bartusiak, in a science article

The idea is, the marriage still exists
when they're at different coasts for the summer:
her job, his ailing parents. Some weeks
even fax- and phone-chat thins
to a nebular frizzle the instruments barely acknowledge.
Even so, she knows she knows she's married and
she *thinks* she knows he knows it too.
She imagines him now, he's walking through the garden
of the house in Palo Verde, in the dawnlight there
that always looks so unsoiled, so
historically uninhabited-through; and in the face
of the coffee and its seemingly prescient tentacles of steam,
he sees the day ahead, a day of salt baths
and colostomy bags, of people one loves monolithically
going grain by grain to something
a son can only sift through, shaking his head.
In a way, although the thought is shameful, she
envies him this: the lug and grunt of working
human necessities—enormous grand pianos
of human distress and their human solutions—across
the convolute rooms of a day. For her, the world is all abstraction
and the iffiness of quarkish nonevents, for her
it's less than air, since air of course is elements
imperturbable and ponderous by her standards
—she's a theoretician of quantum gravity models, and
she uses a machine the size of a shopping mall
to track the ghostly geysering of particles that exist
so far in hypothesis only. It's *beautiful*,
it's *consummatory*, labor; but some mornings
when she walks along the squabble of Atlantic water
and Jersey shore, she feels the need

to hug herself, to keep herself
from suddenly evaporating into the between-states
of her studies. Or to have *somebody*
hug her. That night, at Kelly's Reef,
as a patchwork jazz quartet is into its last set,
Mr. Silk-'n-Sip—a friend of a friend
of a friend, who's magically latched on to their party—
makes the thousand invisible signs of availability.
His hands are shapely and capable. His stories
encompass plasma physics, Van Gogh connoisseurship,
Tantric sex techniques. She's crazy
to say no, but she says no. It's 4 a.m.
and in the rumple of her by-the-month
efficiency apartment, in her sleeplessness,
she idly works the gold ring off her finger, lets the light
trace its solidity, then puffs a single
breath through its empty center. It's late,
she's sleepy at last, she
wraps herself in her blanket, and
if some of it, *somewhere* in it, isn't blanket,
she wraps herself in that too.

Notes from the Desktop

Another poem where Rachel phones in the thick of the night
to tsk her list of insomniac twinges, culminating
in Ned, the shit, her love, the stupid shit, her all-consuming.
Another poem amazed at how the entire unboundaried universe
spirals into the open amino acids of every individual life,
as if the band (what we imagine as a band) of stars
and this stirred morning coffee were concentric rings
of the same machine. The emptiness inside my friends.
The void between the nebulae. Another poem
in which I replace the phone in its cradle, then go upstairs
and softly sidle against my sleeping wife or
pretendingly sleeping wife—how much can even
intimacy tell us of the web of patterned elements we call
another person? And under all of our speeches
stuffed with adult woo and irk, below them
like the psyche's Indo-European, what cursive script
did everybody's fetus-self inscribe in practice spasms
on its nothing and everything walls? Or add more
detail: pinwheel, "*pinwheel* nebulae," "pinwheel nebulae smoldering,"
that's good. Another poem, a tribute (not that he needs more): it's 1905,
it's morning, he stirs his morning coffee. Or make that morning
tea, and not in a cup but in a greenish thick-walled handleless glass
like a jelly jar—set in this earliest light it looks like a murky battery,
from which our pensive but unassuming young clerk (he's 26)
is charging the rest of his day; and in a way, that's true.
The early mornings in Berne are as clear as a polished agate.
This café is nearly empty, the city is mainly asleep,
the idea of world war isn't even invented yet, a tilt of cream
descends the tea with an easy, tentacled gravity.
Our clerk—our boy genius—is busy, humming idly
to himself and busy, his head is a hive of activity, is filling

with that special twentieth-century honey. Another poem
in which he considers the pull of space on time, in this beginning
post-Newtonian cosmos. Simply by thinking, he vivisects
the light as surely as earlier discoverers cut the flesh.
You'd think a morning's work like that would require
the whole of a mind—but he's lovesick with a woman,
the bitch, the dear, the royal bitch, the flame and the flower,
and so his nethermind is all this while wondering
at what Fahrenheit our caring for each other
flashes hopelessly to ash. He can picture her
turning around in the doorway, gaslight skittering
like the keys of a player piano up her naked flank; and
he can picture her turning away. Another poem of skin
attracting skin; of skin repelling skin; of Rachel
torn by sparks. But it's so quiet here; numbers
fall out of the air, oh numbers to the billionth power, more . . .
Another paper in a scientific journal—in this case,
Annalen der Physik, Volume 17. Einstein
whispers her name to the tea. He's going to call it
"On the Electrodynamics of Moving Bodies,"
he's going to gather his scattered notes. The phone rings.
The galaxies fly from each other.

Seriema Song

The flamingo delouses its belly with the easy speed
of a power lawn trimmer. The osprey; the emu; the kiwi . . .
In a glass-paned cage labeled *Toucan / Lemur*,
two new arrivals—red-legged seriema, says a docent—
stalk their confines, querulous and
frantic. One jabs adamantly at a strew of mulch
and feather-molt over the damp ground, and the other,
with a fierce determination better sized to the gorilla
than this shin-high bristled bird, uptussles
a fake plant from its anchorage and then
using its beak as a pliers and hammerclaw, single-mindedly
labors until it frees a formerly-hidden square
of wire screen—a jailbreak, we think, then see
the seriema repeatedly lift the mesh in its beak
and slam it at the ground, again, again, a motion
something like the beating of a fire with a blanket,
and we realize they're attempting to build a nest
in this alien habitat, the seriema expects
this scarf-large square of screen to break apart
eventually into useable shreds. Again. Again.
Each swing and its connection jolts the bird
like live electrodes. Again. The goddam wire screen.
Again. We leave to watch the August heat
curl up inside the lioness's yawn, then turn
to blue lace over the seals' pool, then stand
foursquare to meet the rhino's
lumbrous run head-on. When we return
the bird's still fighting the wire screen.
That night you turn to me: "I bet

(*note*: sairy-émma)

it's *still* beating that screen at the ground."
Lifting it overhead like a professional wrestler
raising an opponent and whomping him
onto the mat. We laugh. We sleep
and the seriema's hitting the screen at the ground.
We wake, we quarrel, and that stupid,
faithful bird is hitting the screen at the ground.
We strive to make the marriage work. We stray
but return to the job of keeping its seams together,
rivet, needle-and-thread. We sweat
and the seriema rises and falls like an oil-well pump,
we dream, we fling ourselves against our dreams,
and the seriema's not done. We lift our fists
to God against the background of that bird. We
watch the news, and sleeplessly turn in the pit
of the news, and enter another day of effort
and salary, effort and the tiny painful
glitches in our friendships, effort and upkeep,
a day made of patchwork and glues, and the bird
is whipping its wire screen against the planet, tireless,
sapbrained, necessary bird, we fret
and it's still at its toil, we soften the abrasive
grain of our love, and it's still at its passionate
task, we're ageing and the seriema, the universe
and the seriema, the face in the mirror,
it's night, its velvet covering us again
and that bird.

The Yoking of the Two Modes

St. Theresa fried eggs during her ecstasies.
                                        Elemire Zolla

Unto us is given a billboard, its spaghetti the size
of transatlantic cable; in the depths of the entangled
weft of this behemothian pasta, passersby discern
the face of Jesus Christ, a face off keyrings and off vigil candles,
now concernedly studious over the traffic jams of Atlanta.
Unto us is given shadow and light, treebark
and shadow and light, and then the visage of The Holy Mother
is born of bark and shadow and light, tenderly
confronting us from an otherwise shabbily
nondescript tree in the Bronx. And the egg . . . ?
In an 18th-century home-art shingle for JAMISON POULTRY GOODS,
the girl—near twelve, I'd guess—is candling one
at an orange flame the painter has made as solid
as a first-prize garlic (flinging teeth of garlic for units
of light). The mix of red in the orange is *so* ferocious,
her face is held by just a missing stroke or two of the brush
from being visionary; as it is, the egg is one
of hundreds of eggs in a crudely-piled tumulus of waiting eggs
behind her, and her face is more like something
turned into a tallying machine for this long,
ordinary labor. And yet the egg
in Piero della Francesca's *Madonna and Child*
with Saints and Angels Adored by Federigo da Montefeltro
is another representational
thing completely: symbolizing resurrection,
it hangs by a golden chain
above its otherworldly convocation,
like the highest, wholest note of soprano devotion
a castrato has provided from a hymn.
What's marriage? what's the Son of the Lord?—a perfect
bivalve, only that. But the egg is the dream
the dream dreams. Unto us is given another fleabite day

amid the cattle dung and the stinking gums of the donkeys,
and here a tantalizing glimpse of the Celestial City
nonetheless takes shape in the tallowy afternoon heat.
Unto us is given a week of stacks of income tax receipts,
and out of such fiduciary mulch who ever knows what
kishke-heaving zeals suddenly blossom? Can it happen
here, among the shots of rye and the brass spittoons,
as someone slurs "Look boys" and with a winking, thespian
exaggeration swallows a pickled egg whole? Yes, even
here it will crawl on its segmented belly, here
it will glow from its tail gland and fan its amazing wings.
In the earliest Japanese myths, when the In and the Yo were not
yet divided, "they formed a mass like an egg"—from this,
our Everything is created. Although it's only another night
of chores for the girl in the farm's small candling shed.
It isn't fair! Her father's at the saloon
with his friends, his high-hat lowbrow friends,
her mother has taken the chaise to Pittfield. Now
it's candle one, then candle the next, then candle
the whole of history. She's lonely. She's that age
where sweetcream beats at your wrists instead of blood,
and a dragonfly on fire is always stitching under your breastbone.
Any more pressure, and she thinks she'd lift
like milkweed and go sailing on a breezy parabola
out of this life forever. But it's candle
the next . . .   and then candle the next . . .   It's crazy.
We want to see God. We are given the egg in its fecal tiara.

A Blank Wide Face

Galen's theory of the circulation of the blood required its passing from the right ventricle, through the wall (the septum cordis), to the left ventricle. *"How did it pass through the* septum, *which seems watertight? Through invisible holes. Leonardo [da Vinci] was so hopelessly obfuscated by this Galenic invention that he was able not only to see these invisible holes but to draw them. It would be hard to find a better example of the limitations even of genius"* (George Sarton, "Art and Science").

Percival Lowell's *Mars* was published in 1895; he had seen 184 canals, meticulously recorded using state-of-the-art equipment at his tailor-built Flagstaff observatory, and checked repeatedly, night after night, under prime "opposition" conditions. He continued recording (and adding to) these canals over sixteen years of rigorous study. *Mars and Its Canals* appeared in 1906, *Mars as the Abode of Life* in 1908. *"Percival Lowell was inspired, enthusiastic, eloquent, and, of course, absolutely wrong"* (John Noble Wilford, *Mars Beckons*).

1.

"Would you like me to read you a poem?"
she asks. He's watching Houston whomp the living *menudo*
out of Seattle—what he wants is one more six-pack
and the assurance of sexual slickeriness post-game.
Already I'm sorry I've made this small, exemplum impasse
one-dimensional. Who am I to imply,
as I think I have, that poetry,
on the level at which she accommodates it, is any nobler
than football, on his? or that *her* interest couldn't be
orgasmoavaricious too, and flickers
increasingly bedroomward? And still,
there is this silence. "Okay"—she interprets it
freely—"I'll read you one of my favorite love poems,
Drink to me only with thine eyes . . ."

2.

. . . *And I will pledge with mine*, Ben Jonson is writing.
Robert Herrick is writing. Shakespeare is busy
dying. John Donne is newly appointed Reader in Divinity
at Lincoln's Inn. Mary Herbert, Countess of Pembroke,
continues her generous patronage of the arts
and her "chymicall studies in her Laborator."
Raleigh is in the Tower. The pox is rampant,
the plague will sniff up your ass like a dog,
tobacco is new, and coffee is new, and medical learning
is little more than parroting ancient guesswork.
While the poets are flogging their roses and moons,
and the globe-hungry boys of the Admiralty are carving up
the New World like a roast goose, in the Lord's Year 1616,
William Harvey can be found in an oaken trough of blood,

3.

on his knees, in search of the sheep's heart
just this minute slipped from its finickily slit casing.
There!—and he pares it by layers thinner
than an onion's umber skins, and finally opens up the secret
fourplex architecture, spasming yet in its residue dampness.
This he's done with the anvil heart of the bullock, as well
as the acorn heart of the dove, and the hare, and the stoat, and the snail,
and the illegally purchased warm corpse of a cutpurse.
In summary: *Galen's theories are incongruous* . . .
There are no pores—that is impossible! Hundreds
of years of inherited wisdom overturned by this thorough man
who's holding his day's work up to the sun now, letting light
travel its chambers. He is, to the body's
red

4.

planet,
what Vikings I and II (1975) become,
to the sky's: ". . . did not discover life
at any level including the microbial, and found no
indication of *canali* existing now or having ever existed."
Finis. And if Percival Lowell *could* be paged
on Albert Goldbarth's famous imaginary life-death
intercom system—could be roused from his mausoleum
under its dome of translucent blue glass, and given his
sentience again—would he weep? would he ball his fists
and pound the Mars-like Arizona ground in frantic mourning
for his dream? or would he grimace, shrug, and then get
back to the daily labor of charting his beautiful
spiderwebbing of undeniable lines? "We see," my mother's

5.

always said in her ditsy, oracular, tautological way,
"what we see." In 1630, the nuns of St. Ligorio witnessed
Joseph of Copertino fly across the length of the church; he
also flew for Pope Urban VIII, the Duke of Medina de Rio-Seco,
the Duke of Brunswick, the Duc de Bouillon, and
a scatter of unnamed shepherds. Seeing *is* believing; also
vice versa. William Drummond says Ben Jonson
"saw in a vision his eldest son, then a child, appear
with the mark of a bloody cross on his forehead"
—the boy had just died. *Oh yes, Ben Jonson . . .   now*
I remember . . .   They're in bed, at last. He's sleeping.
She's not, she's intently awake. She studies
his face, his blank wide face,
and wills what she needs to its surface.

Marriage, and Other Science Fiction

1. A Traveler

A millipede-thing the size of a Brahma bull is devouring
palm fronds that are longer than stretch limos.
He watches the multiplied sun along its segmented armor; then,
again, he works the gleaming Lever.
                                    When the blear and nausea
dissipate, he's on a mossy rise overlooking
a tannery compound (this would make it—what?
12, 1300 A.D.? and the read-out panel confirms this). He
studies a coltish apprentice scouring out a hide
with grabs of pigeon dung rubbed vigorously, but then the breeze
about-faces and the lingering death-stench clobbers him truly
as if it were a pitched rock, so he shoulders into the armlong
Lever yet again, millennia whirring
like slot machine fruit,
                        and when he stops it's snowing
white babushkas about fantastical eyrie cupolas no 20th,
21st, or even 22nd-century eyes would recognize. Then,
floating out of that city's streets: a ululating
of human woe he's come to know, whatever the year, and whatever
the current stage of our inadequate neocortex.

2. Us

You were moaning. It was that low and fluttery
black-leaf-of-a-moan

                              —and so I knew your sister was dying
again. I could have waked you, saved you
from the merciless repeating of that othertime, but
finally saw I had no right to break the painful
peace your dream was making. I stroked your back,
just that—and lightly, not enough to jostle one camellia
in the vase they set on the sill of that room
in your mind, while the terrible turbojet
of her iron lung filled the universe with its roar. Before
you calmed back into an evener sleep, a few of *my*
ghosts skirled around the bedroom darkness, having been
emboldened by your own—and one or two of them really
ugly, they would translate maybe
into primitive sea-life: vampire molluscs . . .

                                              When
I woke, you were stroking my back. The sky
was gray already, tinctured by the iodine smear of dawn.
Your hand was marked by fang-edged seashell imprints.
A black leaf was stuck to my palm.

3. Thirteen

"What if he stopped in some year when they put a building right there,
you know" and Irwin Benovitz flaps his hands "right there
where the Time Machine" flapping in search of an accurate term
"*materialized!* He'd explode or he'd become the bricks of the building
forever, right?"
                    When I look back now at those two, at their urgent
traipse through Wells and endless ill-writ rip-off Wells, their
great hormonally-powered and slightly pathetic enthusiasm
for waking in any tomorrow other than normalcy's, I feel I should
apologize to the other one, the friend—no matter
how many Levers he'll press in his imagination, buttons, dials,
his future is only his becoming
me: a man in a house, who loves his wife, they
go about their daily fracas and deal with their small interfacing
sadnesses as best they can. Maybe he'll forgive me
that; I've tried to make some friendships and a few words
durable—anyway, time is impossible. The melting snowflake
gears of the engine of time. Klein bottle time. The switchback,
serpent-shimmy, parallel traintrack, purl and surd and
do-si-do inscrutable movements of time.
                                          "Yeah and
what if somebody else *was living on that spot?*"
says the friend "*right there*, they became this two-in-one creature,
he opened his eyes surrounded all day by this other person all
        through him?"
First they're silent—then they giggle, it's such
an enormity, and they're thirteen.

4. Forty-four

Silver-plate a cucumber, then equally silverly fin it
like an angelfish: you'd have a spiffy 1990 rocket ship,
by 1930's standards. And that thirteen-year-old boy
I was in 1961?—was raised in that
sci-fi tradition, and is sure the years ahead mean life
in Lunaville (a "bubble city": remember?), its citizens zooming
through the sky on the personal dual jet-blasts
of "fly-tanks" (worn like backpacks) . . .
                                            What
does he think of us now? He's still alive, of course, just
layered-under in a sticky film of 31 succeeding years;
he'll stir, and wake, and find us fretting
over last night's muggers at the corner, and
not pirates on the moon. What would he make
of your cyst? and why, when waiting
late word from your oh-bee-gee-why-en, do I imagine this historic
inchling squirm in me, and dream of the Lever, that powerful
staunch brass scepter with the octahedronal crystal knob,
and its blurry crosstemporal promise . . .
                                            huh? you
use the word "distracted"—as if I were somewhere else.
As if you looked and saw I was missing a hand,
or a nugget of brain, or a radish of meat
from my heart, and what I showed instead was some similar part
of a thirteen-year-old once-me . . .

There's
that lovely fairy tale, six brothers
turned to swans and then turned back to human selves,
except for the youngest, whose spell is incomplete
by some few words, "and like the others he became human again;
but one arm was the wing of a swan."

5. Distance

NOW! Beamish and Stanhope's UNIVERSAL LAP ARMOIRE
meets ALL OF YOUR TRAVEL NEEDS—is Especially Jointed
for Portability—Serve TEA in Wedgwood Cups,
on an inhospitable Himalayan slope! or read your
MR. DICKENS before sleep, in the wilds of Hottentot Africa! . . .

☙

So: there are clever means by which to keep appalling otherness
at safe arm's-length, in distance-travel—"lesser travel,"
the secret corps of Chrononauts sneeringly call it.

                                               For them,
their suddenly being birthed into a new gestalt is
painfully disorienting, far beyond contrivances' remediations.
Once I thought I could study the mackerel-gray or sepia
crowd scenes in, say, turn-of-the-century photographs, and
recognize the rare time-traveler trying to blend indigenously,
by his unconcealable condescension ("Oh, *I* knew this
was going to happen!") but, no; especially on those just arrived,
it's always a central look of horror, and confusion, and
an excitement that feeds on horror. Twice
I've seen a face I thought was Irwin Benovitz's

                                              —once
among a clutch of stern-cheeked hayseed gawkers queuing up
at the flap of Natasha's Tent of Dance Exotique, at a dumpy fair;
and once among a group of conscriptees standing joking, smirking,
a few of them doing a soft-shoe shuffle, waiting on the pier

for the ship that will take them to die in the trenches. I *think*
it was Irwin—after all, it's been 31 years. Maybe
while I grew up and distant, he stayed true to those fancies,
researched them, met others who wore the invisible insignia, and
joined that most elite band of time-trippers; maybe he even
commandeers a Lever, ornate and substantial, and oiled as if
with the silky by-products of all of human evolution,
just as we'd dreamed it. I can't imagine the thrust
of his exits, the rays and webbings he breaks through, or
his entrances into alien worlds. For us, it's confusing enough
to travel ahead in time by 24 hours, bringing
ontogeny's living zoo into a new day: all that
avianswoop and lizardchill that's never left us really, but
must wake sometimes in an incomprehensible future
—the *Homo sapiens* psyche—shrieking, ribboning
mindstuff with its claws . . .
                                        I turn to you, and see
you're still one-half in dream: as if part nude
and part unsculpted marble. Here we are,
7 a.m., on the current submicrodot nano-edge of the Big Bang,
groping at love, in the red shift. How can we travel
through space so *fast*,
we drag such baggage with us?

6. A Traveler / Us

The rain forest tribe, where time goes slow and
partite, like the remnant rain of last night's storm
that still drips, from the leaves, all through the morning . . .
The endless present tense
in which the stale breaths of Hassid scholars
repeat The Word of the Glorious Host of Hosts . . .
The ton of bricks
being hauled toward the recess bell on a schoolroom clock . . .

So many.
I remember the shop
at the bowbend of an impossibly-potholed lane
outside of Grasse: perhaps 200 clocks,
from hand-sized cuckooettes to burnished deeply-tolling
grandfather clocks like sentry boxes, all of them
ticking, each of them keeping—slightly or gigantically—
an independent time. It's like a snowfall
—each flake different, but contributing in synchrony
to something so vast it's beautiful and
serially fierce in its implications, at once . . .
It must be *some* great metaphysical conundrum like this,
that keeps a figure, a man? or a woman?,
staring out a window
through the borders-blurring downfall
of a bitter winter night that could be any bitter winter night
—but is, in this poem, January, 1992.

☞

The Traveler has gingerly parked his Machine
beneath a rocky overhang, and now
he's out walking—gently wafting snow, but thick, and nearly
making linen of the air. The one light
on in our living room calls him—here
might be some clue that specifies the general "when"
of his read-out panel. He approaches not exactly
stealthily, but not forthrightly either; anyway, he's too
cautious to hazard much more than quietly standing in a snowbank
scanning our house from across the yard, so
can't determine anything but a vague, gray figure
staring out into the night and then—as if at someone's
summons—turning back in to the room. A long wait.
Snow, like units for counting a long wait. Then
(and this he could have predicted) the ululation: something vocal
that could easily mean pleasure, or could be a marker
set on the scale between small pique and despair. Do
even *they* know which?—he thinks this is the age
where people "worked at" "marriage," and all of those otherwise
very distinctive concepts overlapped. He
tries to remember: did they tell time by notched bones?
or by monitoring their protein-code mutation? or the cesium atom?
No, no—now he remembers this age.
A "watch," they called it: two hands held a face.